LONGMAN NATURE LIBRARY

WHALES, DOLPHINS, AND SEALS
AND THEIR KIN

Longman

Longman Group Limited
*Longman House, Burnt Mill, Harlow,
Essex CM20 2JE, England
and Associated Companies throughout the world.*

First published 1985

British Library Cataloguing in Publication Data
Whales, dolphins and seals: and their kin. —
(Longman nature library)
1. Marine mammals
599.5   QL713.2

ISBN 0-582-89262-7

Index by Barbara James

Set in MCS 9/10 pt Mallard

Printed in Spain
by TONSA, San Sebastian

CONTENTS

Introduction   6

About this book   20

Seals and Sea Lions   22

Dugongs and Manatees   56

Whales and Dolphins   60

Glossary   120

Further reading   124

Index   125

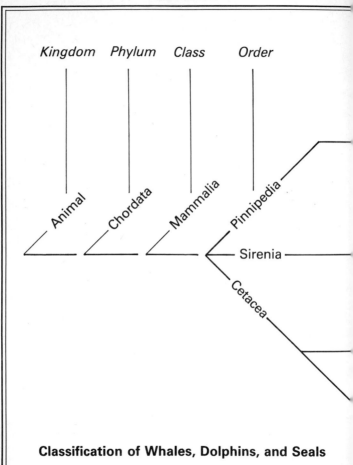

Classification of Whales, Dolphins, and Seals

Family

Otariidae – sea lions or eared seals

Odobenidae – walruses

Phocidae – true seals

Dugongidae – dugongs

Trichechidae – manatees

Platanistidae – river dolphins
Phocoenidae – porpoises
Delphinidae – dolphins
Physeteridae – sperm whales
Monodontidae – white whales
Ziphiidae – beaked whales

toothed whales

Eschrichtidae – grey whales
Balaenopteridae – rorquals
Balaenidae – right whales

baleen whales

INTRODUCTION

Whales, seals, dolphins and their kin are mammals. Most people have an idea of what a mammal is, and this idea is probably quite close to the scientific definition. The name 'mammal' is derived from the Latin *mammalis*, which means 'breast', and mammals characteristically have mammary glands or breasts which produce and secrete the nourishing milk on which baby mammals are suckled.

Mammals are vertebrates, which are those animals that possess a bony or cartilaginous rod running along the back side of the trunk of the animal from the head to the tail region. They are often referred to as being 'warm blooded' although, more correctly, they should be called homoiothermic; in other words, they are able to maintain their internal body temperature at a more or less constant level regardless of the conditions.

Because they need to maintain their body temperatures, the great majority of mammals are covered with an insulating layer of hair; birds are covered with a layer of feathers for the same reason. Mammals also usually have sweat glands in their skin enabling them to cool their bodies by sweating in hot conditions. Most mammals have relatively large brains. Mammals do not lay eggs but give birth to comparatively well-developed young.

These characteristics, together with their typical four-footed method of locomotion and socketed teeth in the jaws, make mammals ideally fitted to a life on land where they first evolved. But there is one group of animals which people sometimes mistakenly regard as fishes because, in some ways, some of them are not dissimilar to large sharks; indeed, even the scientific community thought they were fishes until the late eighteenth century. These are the aquatic or water-dwelling mammals, including the whales, dolphins, seals, walrus, manatees, and dugongs, most of which live in the sea. Although there are many obvious differences between these animals and the terrestrial mammals, they have been clearly recognized as mammals because they resemble their land-based cousins in some very important ways. They are warm blooded, they breathe air using lungs, and they bear well-formed young which, as they grow, are fed by the mother on milk from her mammary glands.

If we take the whales as typical of the sea mammals, it is clear that they have evolved a number of specialized features which enable them to survive in their watery world. They lack a layer of hair because this would impede their progress through the ocean. To compensate for this, they possess a thick layer of blubber. Clearly, the blubber is a very efficient insulating material because whales are able to survive at relatively low temperatures in the depths of the sea or in some of the world's coldest oceans. This blubber also helps to improve their streamlined shape.

Most sea mammals, and especially whales, are large. Indeed, the blue whale, at as much as 30 metres (100 feet) long and weighing in at some 150 tonnes, has long been considered the largest animal ever to have lived on Earth; it is possible, however, that the dinosaur, named *Supersaurus*, was even bigger. Large size gives whales the advantage of high bulk in relation to surface area so that they lose heat more slowly than smaller animals do.

Obviously, the normal mammalian limbs are not

ideally suited for propulsion in the water. Consequently, the fore limbs have become modified into flippers, and the tail has flattened out into a pair of paddle-like tail flukes which provide whales with forward thrust by beating up and down, unlike the sideways motion of the tail fin in fishes. Their hind limbs have disappeared altogether except for remnants of the pelvic bones which are no longer attached to the skeleton. Although the overall shape of the aquatic mammals may be similar, determined by their life styles, these animals do show some important differences in body form and way of life.

Classification of marine mammals

There is a bewildering array of living things occupying planet Earth and, for a better understanding of the living world, scientists have found it convenient to divide this wealth of life into different groups of various sizes. The process by which these scientists, known as taxonomists, classify animals and plants is a complex and exacting one, requiring detailed knowledge of the anatomy, physiology, ecology, evolutionary history, and relationships of the life forms. As more and more is discovered about the natural world, the classification of living things must be constantly modified. It was once thought that all organisms could be divided into two kingdoms - animals and plants. Most modern systems, however, describe as many as five kingdoms. These divisions take account of such factors as the complexity of the creature or plant and the way in which it feeds and provides itself with energy for growth, maintenance, and reproduction. Whatever system is used, though, an animal kingdom is always recognized.

The animal kingdom is divided into a number of major groups called 'phyla' (singular 'phylum'). The phylum known as Chordata contains all the animals, such as fishes, amphibians, birds, reptiles, and mammals, that are characterized by possessing a flexible supporting rod (backbone) in the body at some stage of their life. We have already defined the major features of animals which are recognized as mammals and which are, therefore, included in the 'class' Mammalia. The mammals are further divided into a number of 'orders', such as the Cetacea (whales, dolphins, porpoises, etc), and each order contains a number of 'families'. For example, all the marine dolphins are included in the family Delphinidae while the five species of river dolphins make up the family Platanistidae. In this book, we shall be considering all three orders of aquatic mammals: the Cetacea; the Pinnipedia, containing the seals and walrus; and the Sirenia, containing the sea cows and manatees.

People often wonder why taxonomists have to give things seemingly difficult names consisting of two latinized words, conventionally printed in italics. For example, why should a blue whale be called *Balaenoptera musculus* rather than simply a blue whale? In the eighteenth century, it was the intention of the Swedish naturalist, Carolus Linnaeus (who it was, incidentally, that first recognized these aquatic animals as mammals) to give every living thing a unique scientific name. It is on his original work that our present system is based. For example, the animal which is commonly known in English as the killer whale or orca actually belongs to the family Delphinidae and is, therefore, strictly a dolphin and not a whale. And, of course, it has other common names in different languages but internationally it is known as *Orcinus orca*. These two words also give an indication of the origins, form, and relationships of this animal.

Looking at the scientific name, the porpoises included in the family Phocoenidae, such as the spectacled porpoise or the Dall's porpoise, both belong to the 'genus' *Phocoena* but only the spectacled porpoise, which is a clearly separate 'species', is called *Phocoena dioptrica*. The word *'dioptrica'* is the species name and it is the species which is the basic unit of classification. Essentially, a species is a population of living things which do not differ from one another fundamentally, which do differ from members of another species, and which are able to breed among themselves to produce fertile offspring.

History of the marine mammals

Evolution is now widely regarded as the process whereby, over the vast aeons of geological time, new species of living things emerge while others become extinct in response to changes in the environment. New species are generally thought to have evolved as a result of the mechanism of natural selection. By this means, organisms which are well fitted to their environment tend to survive and reproduce with greater success than animals and plants which are less well adapted.

The origins of aquatic mammals are not well known. It has been suggested that the ancestor of the manatees and dugongs was an animal, descended from an ancestor of modern elephants, which, some 54 to 38 million years ago, fed on sea grass that thrived in shallow tropical waters surrounding the coasts of the western Atlantic and Caribbean areas. Subsequently, the manatees have adapted to feed on the more abrasive grasses which grow in the rivers of West Africa and the Amazon basin. Their front teeth are continually shed and replaced from the rear - a process similar to that which occurs in elephants.

The earliest-known whale-like fossils are called archaeocetes. They, too, seem to have occurred as long ago as 54 million years and are very similar to modern toothed whales. In turn, these may have evolved about 60 million years ago from a group of land-living meat eaters called mesonychids. The first of the toothed whales had certainly appeared by about 40 million years ago, during the epoch of geological time known as the Eocene, whereas the baleen whales had to wait until about 25 to 30 million years ago before they arrived on the scene.

The eared seals or sea lions, the walrus, and the true seals, all included in the order Pinnipedia, probably evolved from two separate groups and are, therefore, not a natural group so far as classification is concerned. The eared seals and the walrus probably developed from meat-eating animals similar to dogs about 25 million years ago, that is, during the Miocene epoch. The true seals, on the other hand, appeared rather later, about 15 million years ago, and are thought to have evolved from otter-like carnivores. Thus, three separate groups of mammals, derived from quite different ancestors, have evolved from land-living animals to find a niche in water.

Some 65 million years ago, at the end of the Cretaceous period, a major upheaval seems to have taken place among the living organisms on Earth with many major groups of animals becoming extinct. The reason for this continues to puzzle scientists but the most likely explanation seems to be that, for some reason (perhaps even a meteor impact), the climate of the Earth changed dramatically. As a consequence, animals, such as the dinosaurs, disappeared from the land while, in the sea, the marine reptiles, like the plesiosaurs and ichthyosaurs, met their end. During this time, the mammals were evolving rapidly, and it may have been that natural selection favoured those species which were able to adapt to feed upon the aquatic food no longer exploited by the reptiles, particularly as competition on land increased.

Distribution

The whales are widely distributed throughout all the major oceans of the world, occupying habitats that range from the very deep seas to shallow coastal waters and even some river estuaries in the case of the primitive river dolphins. The eared seals and sea lions are rather more restricted in their distribution and preferred habitat. They are mostly coastal animals distributed around northern Pacific coasts, the coasts of South America and South Africa, the southern coasts of Australasia, and some oceanic islands including the Galapagos and those of the Antarctic. The walrus is confined mainly to the pack ice of the Arctic seas. The true seals of the family

Phocidae are found mainly on the pack ice, as well as continental ice, throughout the seas surrounding the Arctic and Antarctic regions as well as around the coasts of more temperate areas, such as northern Europe; there are even some species which live in the Mediterranean and around the islands of the Caribbean and Hawaii. The sea cows and manatees, on the other hand, are restricted to river estuaries and coasts around the western side of northern South America and southern North America, as well as south-east Asia, northern Australia, and the East and West African coasts.

Habits

All animals need to find enough food of the right kind to be able to live, grow, and reproduce, otherwise individuals and eventually the species would die out. There are some 113 species of aquatic mammals each of which is well adapted to its own particular niche.

The whales and dolphins of the order Cetacea are the most specialized for life in the sea. They are beautifully shaped for propelling themselves efficiently through the water and all of the organs which would project from the body of a land-living mammal have been adapted to their streamlined bodywork. There are no external ears, the male penis is contained within the abdomen, and the female mammaries are encased within slits. Some species have developed a fatty fin on their backs and they all have fore limbs modified as fins which aid in steering.

There are two main groups of cetaceans: the toothed whales, which include the dolphins, porpoises, white whales, sperm whales, and beaked whales; and the baleen whales. Instead of teeth, the baleen whales possess a sieve-like structure of horny plates which grow from the sides of the upper jaw and are derived from the ridges which cross the upper palate of many mammals. To accommodate these baleen plates, (usually referred to as 'whalebone' even though they are not made of bone at all) the jaws of baleen whales are extended. And the baleen plates themselves, which may be of different lengths in different species, are fringed with bristles to aid in trapping food. It is always surprising to learn that such gigantic animals feed on the tiny animals collectively known as plankton, in particular, the larger, reddish-coloured shrimp-like creatures, called krill, which are present in vast quantities in the waters of the Antarctic. Effectively, the krill are filtered from the water by the baleen plates; then the whale presses its tongue against the palate, forcing out water and leaving the salty krill 'high and dry' so that it can be swallowed.

The different species of toothed whales feed on a wide variety of prey, ranging from molluscs and crustaceans to fishes, and even other sea mammals. Their carnivorous ancestors, well adapted to catch, kill, and devour their land-living prey, had teeth which are similar to those found in modern meat eaters, such as dogs. In other words, they possessed chisel-shaped incisors for biting, the killing canines, and the grinding molars. This type of dentition is not ideally suited to catching a slippery fish, and the fish-eating species of whales have rows of small, sharp, even, conically shaped teeth. Others, such as the killer whale, which also eats mammals, have smaller numbers of larger teeth while the species that feed mainly on squid have very few teeth. In fact, the narwhal has only two teeth, neither of which is used in feeding; in males, one of these grows to form a long, unicorn-like tusk which may be used in courtship or territorial displays. This tusk may be as much as 3 metres (10 feet) long. The narwhal feeds on a diet of crustaceans, fishes, and squid, and it seems to have some suction-like ability to capture its prey.

To obtain their food, many whales dive to remarkable depths where there is little light and at which the water pressure is very great. They are mammals and need to breathe air, so how do they stay under water for such long periods? How, too, can they locate their prey, or even hunt co-operatively, in the darkness close to the sea bed? Surprisingly, even the largest whales have comparatively small lungs but, even on just one lungful of air, some species can stay submerged for more than an hour. Nor do whales suffer from the problem which has plagued human deep-sea divers - the bends. This condition is caused by nitrogen, which has dissolved in the blood under deep-sea pressures, forming bubbles as the diver returns to the surface. It can cause extreme pain and can be very dangerous. But, in comparison with the size of the animal, the amount of air and, therefore, the amount of nitrogen, which a whale takes with it as it dives, is quite small. In addition, the lungs are evacuated and any nitrogen is thought to be absorbed by an oily foam secreted by glands in the air passages. To maintain the continued functioning of the muscles and other organs on a restricted supply of oxygen, the whale's tissues contain special substances which act as an oxygen reserve.

Finally, to allow them to 'see' in the dark, whales

have extremely acute hearing and they communicate with one another by producing a variety of sounds which can carry very long distances in the sea. It has been suggested that, with the development of motor-driven ships and the increased ocean traffic, whale communication systems have been disrupted, and this may even be one of the reasons for the decline of many species. Toothed whales have a sonar system, similar to that used by bats, which enables them to find and capture prey. Like bats, they produce pulses of high-frequency sound which bounce off objects and provide them with a very accurate picture of their surroundings.

Unlike the whales and the members of the Sirenia, the seals and sea lions are not wholly aquatic and must return to land to breed. Most of their food, however, is taken in the water. These sea mammals feed on a wide variety of prey which they capture as the opportunity arises. Thus, their food ranges from fishes to clams, squid, and other molluscs, krill and other crustaceans, aquatic mammals including seals, and even seabirds, such as penguins. Their powerful jaws and sharp teeth are used to grasp and subdue the prey, which is then usually swallowed whole. Some species specialize in particular diets; for example, the crabeater seal eats mainly krill, the walrus eats mainly molluscs, and the leopard seal preys mainly on other seals and penguins.

The dugongs and manatees comprise a quite unique group of aquatic mammals in that they feed entirely on plant material for which they compete only with sea turtles, unlike their plant-eating counterparts on land. They are usually slow movers and live in relatively warm seas so that their energy needs are comparatively low, which is just as well for the sea grasses which they eat are not very nutritious. They do not chew the cud like cattle but feed rather more like elephants or horses. Somehow, these strange creatures have given rise to stories of mermaids although they can hardly be regarded as beautiful except perhaps by another sea cow!

Human threats to the sea mammals

The sea has often been regarded by humans as an inexhaustible source of food and other materials. And the aquatic mammals have certainly not escaped man's attention. In recent years, the plight of whales in particular has captured the public imagination throughout many countries of the world. For thousands of years, whales have been hunted to provide meat, oil, and whalebone while seals were sought for their skins and blubber to provide clothing, food, and oil for lamps. Even the common name of one whale, the right whale, derives from its unfortunate fate at the hands of whalers. It was the 'right whale' to hunt because it was slow moving and vulnerable to the hand-held harpoon, and because its body floated after death.

The sea cows are harmless and slow moving; their meat is considered a delicacy; and they breed slowly so that their existence is now threatened. Dolphins are often caught in the nets of fishing vessels and seals have been mercilessly culled on the grounds that they compete for the fish which humans also seek. Not least among the threats to the aquatic mammals is pollution. Because they are at the top of the ocean food chains, some species of seals, in particular, tend to concentrate any toxic wastes in their blubber, and contamination by oil slicks may cause some species to lose heat. In our ever-increasing demand for food, it may be that even the oceans' vast stocks of krill may soon be severely depleted with dire consequences for the remaining small numbers of the krill-eating whales, despite the ban on all commercial whaling which, as a result of public pressure, comes into effect in 1986. The aquatic mammals are thought to be highly intelligent creatures but even this has led them to be exploited by humans as circus animals in dolphinariums or even as living torpedoes for military use. It is to be hoped that, as humans learn more and more about the sea and the creatures which inhabit it, greater care will be taken to maintain the rich and complex web of marine life so that these magnificent creatures will continue to grace the seas of the world.

ABOUT THIS BOOK

There are some 4000 species of mammals distributed around the world, ranging in size from the tiny, nocturnal pygmy shrews to giant sea mammals, such as the blue whale. Of the 4000, there are about 113 species of more or less fully aquatic mammals. These are divided into three orders and include seventy-six species of whales and dolphins, thirty-three species of seals and sea lions, and just four species of manatees and dugongs. Many sea mammals are in danger of extinction and there is one famous documented case of the Steller's sea cow which was totally wiped out only twenty-seven years after its first discovery on Copper Island in 1741. The significance of mammals generally is heightened because they are relatively large and conspicuous and, of course, humans are mammals, too. But the aquatic mammals occupy a very special place in our planet's complex web of life.

Whales, Dolphins, and Seals has been designed to describe and illustrate a representative selection of these, often hauntingly beautiful, creatures to show the ways in which each has become so well fitted to pursue its own particular life style. In general body form, they may all seem similar to one another but there are important differences in their biology which this book seeks to highlight. It has not been possible to describe every species of water-dwelling mammal in this one volume but at least one member of each of the fourteen families has been included.

This is not a field guide but, using the fine illustrations and concise but authoritative descriptions in tandem, it should be possible to decide to which family any one of these creatures belongs. In addition, if you read through the book, it will give you a good general catalogue of the various types of aquatic mammals which enhance the oceans of the world.

Seals and Sea Lions
ORDER PINNIPEDIA

There are some thirty-three species, contained within three families in the order Pinnipedia or 'wing-footed' mammals. The fourteen species of sea lions and fur seals, otherwise referred to as the eared seals, make up the family Otariidae. The walrus has a family all to itself, the Odobenidae, and the true or hair seals comprise eighteen species in the family Phocidae - it is possible that there may be a nineteenth species, the Caribbean monk seal which may or may not be extinct.

They are all carnivorous or meat-eating animals which evolved from land-living carnivores to become well adapted to life in the water. Unlike the whales, they still retain four limbs although these have become modified as flippers for propulsion and steering. Again, unlike the whales, they do not spend all of their time in the water and they have to return to land to breed where they are able to move, albeit awkwardly.

The sea lions and fur seals all have external ears or scroll-like ear flaps; they have an insulating coat of hair made up of bundles of guard hairs and shorter fur; and they are much more agile on land than the true seals because of their ability to tuck the hind flippers fowards while supporting their weight on the front flippers. Their streamlined torpedo-like shape is similar to that of the other members of the order. They haul out on to land to breed in spring and early summer and they are highly gregarious on their traditional breeding sites, the males competing for territories at the rookeries. Like all the pinnipeds, they are vulnerable to predators while they are on land.

Mating takes place only days after the cows have given birth to the young which were conceived in the previous breeding season. This means that breeding and rearing young, as well as mating, can all take place in a single relatively short period on land before they return to the sea. To enable such a long gap to occur between fertilization and birth, without the developing pups growing too large in the womb, the embryo lies dormant for some time before it starts to develop. Male sea lions are larger than females with more bulbous heads and often with a hairy mane.

The walrus seems to be quite closely related to the sea lions and can also bring its hind flippers forwards as it moves on land. Its most characteristic features are the long white tusks and the moustache of whiskers. Sadly, its tusks almost led to the walrus's extinction through hunting about 100 years ago; the ivory can only be compared to that of the elephant in quality and size. Walruses are gregarious although male and female populations are entirely separate at certain seasons.

The true seals lack external ear flaps and are the most fully adapted of all the pinnipeds to life in the water. Unlike the eared seals, they cannot tuck their hind flippers forwards and movement on land is very restricted. They are very mobile in water, however, and have developed remarkable adaptations to enable them to remain submerged for long periods and to dive deeply in search of their food. During a deep dive, the heart rate falls although the blood pressure remains the same because the flow of blood is restricted to the vital organs only.

South American Fur Seal

The South American fur seal has a dense undercoat of deep reddish-brown fur beneath the guard hairs. The coat extends to the parts of the fore flippers which would be close to the wrist of a human hand. It makes a wavy hair line at this point and this is one of the characteristic features of the fur seals of this genus which are all rather similar in appearance. The coat on the underside is generally a rather paler colour. This member of the sea lion family has a rather flattened forehead and quite a long, distinct muzzle. The males are very much larger than the females and may be as much as three times heavier.

They live along the coasts of the South Pacific and Atlantic Oceans from southern Brazil around to as far north as Peru where they like to haul out on rocky coasts and islands; they occur in especially large numbers around the Falklands. Their diet includes a variety of marine invertebrates, such as crustaceans and squid, as well as fish and even penguins.

At the breeding sites during November, the males compete vigorously with one another for the best territories. About two weeks later the females arrive, and start giving birth to their pups conceived in the previous season. After a further week, the males that have claimed and held the best sites are able to mate with the most females. The female stays with her pup for about twelve days after it has been born and then returns to sea to feed. She continues to suckle her pup at intervals for about six months. The youngster is usually a black or dark brown colour.

Order Pinnipedia - seals and sea lions (about 33 species)
Family/Species Otariidae - eared seals or sea lions (about 14 species)/South American Fur Seal *Arctocephalus australis*
Length 1.4-1.9 m (4.6-6.25 ft)

Northern Fur Seal

The northern or Alaskan fur seal is a short-muzzled animal and may be distinguished from the other members of the family by its unusually large rear flippers. The adults are generally dark brown or blackish in colour and usually appear all black when they are wet. Both males and females are also characterized by a paler, silvery grey patch on the neck and the young animals are usually grey above with a reddish-brown underside. The males are usually darker in colour than the females and have a heavy mane. Again the male is much larger than the female and may be as much as four times heavier.

The northern fur seal occupies the Bering and Okhotsk Seas between the Alaskan coast of North America and the north-eastern coasts of Russia. Except in the breeding season, from June to September, this sea lion spends most of its time at sea, feeding either singly or in pairs mainly on fish or squid. At different ages, in different parts of their range, or at different times of the year, however, their diet may vary.

The northern fur seals breed on islands throughout their range but the main breeding population of almost 1.5 million animals can be found on the Pribilof Islands with smaller numbers on the Aleutians. The males haul out and establish breeding territories before the females arrive to give birth to their pups conceived in the last breeding season. About a week later mating takes place while the female continues to suckle her young for about a month. At the end of the breeding season, most of the populations migrate southwards for the winter.

Order Pinnipedia - seals and sea lions (about 33 species)
Family/Species Otariidae - eared seals or sea lions (about 14 species)/Northern Fur Seal (Alaskan Fur Seal) *Callorhinus ursinus*
Length 1.4-2.1 m (4.6-6.9 ft)

California Sea Lion

Because it is so readily trained and is appealing to look at, the California sea lion is a popular performer in circuses and marine shows. They are generally a dark chestnut-brown colour when dry although the females and young may be a paler tan hue and both sexes appear nearly black when wet. The animal has a rather long, dog-like muzzle which may be a lighter colour in the male. The male also has a horny crest on its head which serves to distinguish it from the much more lightly built female. Although the male does have a mane around its head and neck, it is much less obvious than in the rather larger Steller sea lion.

It occurs around the Pacific coast of North America from British Columbia to Mexico and including the Galapagos Islands. At one time, there was a subspecies of this sea lion to be found around the coast of Japan but this population is now thought to be extinct. It is a more social animal than some other species of sea lions and will haul out on land even outside the breeding season. Although it is commonly kept in captivity, where it is usually fed on fish, its diet and feeding habits in the wild are not well known. It is thought to feed both at night and during the day, making the most of whatever fish, squid, and octopus come its way.

Although the males arrive at the breeding sites before the females, they do not claim their poorly defined territories until the females arrive and give birth to their single young conceived during the last breeding season. Mating takes place a few days later. The female may suckle her pup for between six and twelve months.

Order Pinnipedia - seals and sea lions (about 33 species)

Family/Species Otariidae-eared seals or sea lions (about 14 species)/California Sea Lion *Zalophus californianus*

Length 1.7-2.2 m (5.6-7.2 ft)

Australian Sea Lion

Males and females of the Australian sea lion generally differ somewhat in colour with the male being an overall dark brown while the female grades from silvery grey on the upper side to brown or yellowish beneath. The male, which is larger than the female, also has a noticeable mane of long, coarse hairs around his neck and shoulders.

The two or three thousand animals of the population are to be found around the coasts and islands off the coasts of southern and south-western Australia where they remain throughout their lives. They are quite agile movers on land and will haul out throughout the year, even hunting and killing penguins for food. Australian fur seals are social animals and may often be seen in small groups. Individuals rarely travel far from the beach on which they were born. Little is known about their diet but they probably eat mainly fish and squid, and they have been seen taking fish from fishermen's nets.

At the beginning of the breeding season, the males claim a strictly defined territory which they defend fiercely against potential rivals. The females in a male's harem are prevented from leaving his territory. The female gives birth to a single chocolate-brown pup, conceived in the previous breeding season, and then mates about a week later. She remains with her pup for about twelve days and then returns to the sea to feed. She will continue to suckle her offspring at about two-day intervals, however, right through until the next breeding season or even longer. Indeed, she may feed it for as long as two years by which time the pup is almost as big as she is.

Order Pinnipedia - seals and sea lions (about 33 species)
Family/Species Otariidae - eared seals or sea lions (about 14 species)/Australian Sea Lion *Neophoca cinerea*
Length 1.5-2.4 m (5-8 ft)

Steller Sea Lion

The Steller sea lion is the largest member of the family, with a big male weighing as much as 1000 kilograms (1 ton) - nearly four times heavier than a small female. In addition to its large size, it is also paler in colour than the California sea lion with a light, reddish-brown coat. Full-grown males have a heavy mane around their neck and shoulders. It inhabits the northern Pacific Ocean from the sea of Japan northwards and from Alaska to the coast of California so that, in part of its range, it overlaps with the California sea lion. The total population of this animal is thought to be about a quarter of a million individuals.

It feeds on a wide variety of food including fish, squid, octopus, molluscs, shrimps, crabs, and even the pups of northern fur seals. Examination of the stomach contents of dead animals has shown that Steller sea lions may dive to depths of as much as 180 metres (600 feet) in search of their food.

The main breeding sites are on the Kurile, Pribilof, and Aleutian islands as well as on the coasts of North America and as far south as San Miguel Island off the coast of California. The males haul out first and establish well-defined territories which they defend vigorously by threatening one another. A short time after the females arrive, each gives birth to a single dark-brown or black pup which she usually suckles for between eight and eleven months (occasionally, females have been observed still feeding two-year-old youngsters). She is mated during the five to thirteen days that she remains with her pup. After that she goes back to sea to feed although the males may stay on the breeding ground for as long as two months.

Order Pinnipedia - seals and sea lions (about 33
  species)
Family/Species Otariidae - eared seals or sea lions
  (about 14 species)/Steller Sea Lion *Eumetopias
  jubata*
Length 2.4-2.9 m (8-9.5 ft)

Walrus

Although the walrus is a member of the order Pinnipedia and resembles the sea lions of the family Otariidae in that it can tuck its hind flippers forward to help it move, it is sufficiently different from all the other members of the order to be granted a family of its own. It varies considerably in size from region to region but the biggest individuals are certainly the largest of the pinnipeds reaching as much as 3.5 metres (11.5 feet) in length and 1200 kilograms (2600 pounds) in weight for a big male. Apart from its huge size, the most characteristic features of the walrus are its heavy tusks which are actually greatly extended upper canine teeth which grow downwards below the lower jawbone. These are longest and most impressive in the males but the females have them, too. Walruses vary in colour from a rich reddish or yellowish brown to a paler yellowish brown and they are generally darker on the undersides. The flippers are naked but the thick, creased skin is covered with coarse hair on the rest of the body.

They are distributed throughout the seas of the Arctic from eastern Canada and Greenland to western Europe and Asia and western Alaska where they occupy the pack ice and rocky islands. They feed largely on a diet of bottom-living molluscs.

They are social animals throughout the year but, during the mating season, the males compete fiercely for their territories sometimes inflicting terrible wounds on one another. The females usually give birth to a single pup which is cared for very gently and may be suckled for up to two years.

Order Pinnipedia - seals and sea lions (about 33 species)
Family/Species Odobenidae - walruses (1 species)/Walrus *Odobenus rosmarus*
Length 2.2-3.5 m (7.2-11.5 ft)

Grey Seal

With the exception of the elephant seal, the grey seal is the largest member of the family Phocidae, and the males may weigh in at as much as 330 kilograms (730 pounds), that is, almost twice as heavy as the females. The male is a much heavier-built animal than the more dainty female, with broad shoulders covered by folds of thick skin which may bear the scars of territorial combats with other males during the breeding season. He also has a longer and wider muzzle as well as a rounded forehead. The male is generally darker and more heavily spotted than the female which is darker above than it is on its spotted underside.

The grey seal mainly occupies the northern part of the Atlantic Ocean although it has been sighted as far south as southern Portugal. Like the other true seals, it is better adapted to life in the water than the eared seals and sea lions but it does haul out to mate on land around the rocky coasts of Britain, Scandinavia, Iceland and the Faroe Islands, Labrador, the Gulf of St Lawrence, and Newfoundland. It swims with a side to side movement of its hind end while the front flippers are used largely for steering. It feeds on a diet of molluscs, crustaceans, squid, octopus, and quite large bottom-living fishes which it catches mainly in the coastal waters where it spends most of its time.

Unlike the sea lions, it is female grey seals which arrive at the breeding sites first to give birth to their white-coated pups. The pups are suckled for two or three weeks, and then the female mates again before returning to sea. The males do occupy breeding territories which may be moved from day to day.

Order Pinnipedia - seals and sea lions (about 33 species)
Family/Species Phocidae - true seals (18 species)/Grey Seal (Atlantic Seal) *Halichoerus grypus*
Length 1.6-2.3 m (5.3-7.6 ft)

Harp Seal

The harp seal is a comparatively slender-looking animal with a less noticeable size difference between males and females than in some other species. As its streamlined shape suggests, it is very active in the water and is an expert swimmer and diver. Indeed, it is particularly noted for its ability to dive to considerable depths, staying submerged for prolonged periods in search of its food of fishes, shrimps and crustaceans including krill. It gets its name from the distinctive harp- or U-shaped dark band along the back and flanks of its otherwise mainly pale-grey body; it also has a black head. The coloration develops more slowly and is less marked in females than in males.

The harp seal is found in the arctic and subantarctic waters of the north Atlantic and Arctic Oceans where it often makes regular north to south migrations, spending the summer in large groups. The total population of these animals is between 2.5 and 4 million individuals. Although they spend most of the year at sea, and normally mate in the water, they do haul out on to ice floes. It is on the ice around northern Russia, Scandinavia, Labrador, and Newfoundland that the females form whelping groups and give birth to their white-coated pups in late February and March. The offspring are suckled on rich, fatty milk by their mothers for about two weeks, after which the females mate, feed for a few weeks, and then migrate northwards for the summer. Before mating the courting males engage in courtship displays and combats.

Order Pinnipedia - seals and sea lions (about 33 species)
Family/Species Phocidae - true seals (18 species)/ Harp Seal *Pagophilus groenlandicus*
Length 1.6-1.9 m (5.3-6.25 ft)

Leopard Seal

With its unusually long, slim, streamlined shape, the leopard seal is especially speedy in the water, which it needs to be in order to pursue and capture its prey of penguins and other seals. It is the only seal that feeds mainly on warm-blooded prey, but it also eats some fishes and crustaceans, including krill. The large head has long jaws containing a formidable set of saw-edged cheek teeth which it uses to seize its food and then tear off the skin before swallowing it. Its coat is essentially grey in colour, but it is darker above than beneath, and the dark spotting is concentrated around the neck, shoulders, and sides. Like other southern ocean seals, the female tends to be longer and heavier than the male.

The leopard seal is found mainly around the edges of the pack ice, coasts, and islands of the southern ocean although it has been observed as far north as Australia, South Africa, and northern Argentina. It is a solitary and nomadic animal.

The breeding biology of this animal is not well known but it is thought that mating takes place between January and March after the females have given birth to their pups in November and December. The pups are a similar colour to the adults and they may be suckled by their mothers for about four weeks but this is not known for certain. Males have not been observed to congregate with females on the pack ice.

Order Pinnipedia - seals and sea lions (about 33 species)
Family/Species Phocidae - true seals (18 species)/Leopard Seal *Hydrurga leptonyx*
Length 2.8-3.5 m (9.2-11.5 ft)

Common Seal

Unlike the leopard seal, the common or harbour seal has a comparatively short body and short flippers but it also has a relatively large head which, in big males, is somewhat domed. The muzzle is dog like. Its coat colour varies but is essentially grey with spots and blotches which may be varying shades of grey, brown or black. The coat of the newborn pup is mainly whitish. Males are usually slightly larger than females.

The common seal is found in the temperate to subarctic coastal waters of the northern Atlantic and Pacific Oceans although it has been seen as far south as Florida and the Azores. The adults do not usually migrate, remaining around the coast, and often hauling out on to rocks as they are revealed by the falling tide. They are also found on mud banks in estuaries and sometimes travel upstream and into freshwater lakes.

They feed mainly during the day on a diet of bottom-dwelling and migratory fishes as well as some squid, molluscs, and crustaceans for which they are able to make dives lasting as long as half an hour. Like the grey seals, they seem to be very inquisitive creatures when humans approach them.

Like most of the other seals in this family, apart from the grey and elephant seals, they court and mate in the water. The pups are relatively mature when they are born, usually during late spring although births may occur at any time between January and September. The female gives birth to a single offspring which is able to swim straight away although it is closely guarded by its mother and suckled for between two and six weeks.

Order Pinnipedia - seals and sea lions (about 33 species)
Family/Species Phocidae - true seals (18 species)/ Common Seal (Harbour Seal) *Phoca vitulina*
Length 1.5-1.8 m (5-6 ft)

Crabeater Seal

The crabeater seal may well be the world's commonest pinniped with a population which probably exceeds 15 million animals. In its remote habitat throughout the pack ice of the Antarctic, there is little to threaten the crabeater seal except killer whales and leopard seals. A slim-looking seal with a small head, its coat is usually a pale grey colour although it may sometimes be darker, especially on the upper parts, while young animals may be rather mottled, and the newborn pups may have a soft coat of brownish or greyish fur. Males and females are approximately the same size. The mature adults are often badly scarred as a result of combats with other crabeaters and from their efforts to escape the attentions of hunting leopard seals. In fact, they are able to move at speeds of up to 25 kilometres an hour (15.5 miles per hour) across the ice to avoid their enemies.

Despite their name, crabeater seals feed mainly on a diet of krill which they sieve from the water through their elaborately shaped, intermeshing teeth, but they also eat squid and some fishes.

The female gives birth to her pup on the ice between about September and December, and she and the offspring are accompanied by the male until mating occurs. The pup is suckled by its mother for four or five weeks, and then young crabeaters may congregate in groups for protection.

Order Pinnipedia - seals and sea lions (about 33 species)
Family/Species Phocidae - true seals (18 species) /Crabeater Seal *Lobodon carcinophagus*
Length 2-2.4 m (6.6-8 ft)

Bearded Seal

As its name suggests, the characteristic feature of this robustly built pinniped is the beard of long, dense, crimpled whiskers around its nose. Its coat is generally a greyish or brownish colour above, sometimes with a few indistinct spots, while it is paler beneath. Males and females are roughly the same size although the females may be slightly longer than the males. It occurs in the shallow waters of the Arctic Ocean although it has been found as far south as northern Spain. It feeds mainly on a diet of bottom-dwelling invertebrates, including molluscs, crustaceans, and sea cucumbers, as well as some fishes.

During the breeding season, in March and April, the males display vocally under water. The females haul out on to pack ice to give birth to a single dark-brown-coated pup which is well developed and can swim straight away. The mother suckles her offspring for between twelve and eighteen days - two weeks on average - and, during this period, she mates again. Unusually, for a northern species of seal, the female bearded seal has four mammary glands rather than the normal two.

Order Pinnipedia - seals and sea lions (about 33
  species)
Family/Species Phocidae - true seals (18
  species)/Bearded Seal *Erignathus barbatus*
Length 2.1-2.4 m (7-8 ft)

Northern Elephant Seal

With the extraordinary trunk-like nose developed by the mature males, it is easy to see how the two species of elephant seals get their name. These are the largest of the pinnipeds with males, at a massive 2700 kilograms (almost 3 tons), weighing nearly three times as much as the females. The greater part of the weight of a male elephant seal is accounted for by blubber which, in turn, is covered by hide that is thick and wrinkled, especially around the neck and shoulders. Adult males may be heavily scarred around their necks from the bites inflicted on them by the large canine teeth of their rivals during the breeding season. These marine mammals are a fairly uniform grey colour although they are more silvery when young.

Northern elephant seals are found along the Pacific coast of North America where they breed mainly on the coastal islands of California as well as on the mainland. In the nineteenth century, these large seals were driven almost to extinction by commercial sealing but now they are protected. Diving deeply for their food, elephant seals eat fishes and some squid.

During November, the males haul out on to the beaches and begin their combats for social dominance before the females arrive a couple of weeks later. Inflating the nasal chamber to enhance their roars, the males display vocally as well as engaging in neck-banging and biting fights. A single dominant male may mate with as many as eighty females after each has given birth to a single pup which is suckled for about four weeks. After breeding and moulting, they tend to move northwards.

Order Pinnipedia - seals and sea lions (about 33 species)
Family/Species Phocidae - true seals (18 species)/ Northern Elephant Seal *Mirounga angustirostris*
Length 3-6 m (10-20 ft)

Mediterranean Monk Seal

The Mediterranean monk seal prefers to haul out on remote, undisturbed rocky islets and cliffs which, as tourism and affluence in the region increase, are now becoming increasingly rare in the areas of the western Atlantic, Mediterranean, Aegean, and Black Sea where it lives. Consequently, its numbers have been greatly reduced, perhaps to as low as 500 individuals, and, because the mothers are so wary, it has been forced to give birth to its young in caves and other cavern-like recesses. Sadly, too, they often become tangled in the nets of fishermen. In colour, its coat is dark brownish above and pale below, even with a very pale or almost white patch. The females are usually slightly longer and heavier than the males. It probably feeds mainly on quite large fishes and some squid.

The breeding biology of this pinniped is not well known but they probably mate in the water and, provided their young are not spontaneously aborted as a result of disturbance, a single black-coated pup is born during the period from May to November. The majority of births seem to occur in September and October. The pup is suckled for six to seven weeks but stays with its mother for three years. Cows bear pups only once every two years and this slow rate of breeding has contributed to the decline of the species.

Order Pinnipedia - seals and sea lions (about 33 species)
Family/Species Phocidae - true seals (18 species)/ Mediterranean Monk Seal *Monachus monachus*
Length 2.3-2.7 m (7.5-9 ft)

Weddell Seal

As its name suggests, the comparatively large Weddell seal spends most of its time living beneath the ice of the near-freezing waters of Antarctica, especially the Weddell Sea. Like the other marine mammals, it must breathe air and, although it is adapted to dive to depths of as much as 600 metres (2000 feet) and can remain submerged for more than an hour, it must then return to the surface to take a gulp of air. There may be pockets of air trapped beneath the ice but, often, the Weddell seal saws a breathing hole through the ice with its teeth. It must be able to navigate sufficiently well to find these holes in the darkness. Its teeth become very worn and, as they are not replaced, it is thought that old seals may die from drowning when they are no longer able to cut through the ice. Weddell seals have a mottled greyish coat which is darker above than below. The females are larger than the males but both have an attractive, small, short-nosed head. They feed mainly on Antarctic cod and other fishes as well as some invertebrates.

Between September and November, the females give birth on the fast ice to a single brownish-grey pup which they suckle for about six weeks, staying with the youngster all the time for about the first twelve days. After the pup has been weaned, the females are mated by the males which have established underwater territories possibly defined by breathing holes through the ice.

Order Pinnipedia - seals and sea lions (about 33 species)
Family/Species Phocidae - true seals (18 species)/ Weddell Seal *Leptonychotes weddelli*
Length 2.5-2.9 m (8.2-9.5 ft)

Hooded Seal

Male and female hooded seals are similarly coloured in grey blotched with black, with a blackish head. The male is generally larger than the female and is characterized by his extraordinary nasal displays. He is able to force the lining of either nostril out through the other nostril like a large red balloon and, in addition, he can also inflate the whole of the nasal hood or chamber above the muzzle into a black-coloured bladder rather like that of the elephant seal. Hooded seals spend most of their time in the open arctic and subarctic waters of the North Atlantic Ocean although it has been found breeding as far south as southern Portugal. This seal feeds mainly on deep-water fishes and squid.

In summer, hooded seals migrate to areas off the east coast of Greenland and to the Denmark Strait where they haul out on to the pack ice to moult. The moult completed, they disperse only to gather again at the breeding grounds - especially in the Gulf of St Lawrence and around north-eastern Newfoundland - during the following March and April. The females give birth to their silvery grey, black-backed pups on ice floes. The mother suckles her young for about a fortnight. During this time she is attended from the water by the male who drives off any rivals by vocal displays and fights, usually underwater but, if necessary, on land. He then mates with the female about two weeks after she has given birth.

Order Pinnipedia - seals and sea lions (about 33 species)
Family/Species Phocidae - true seals (18 species)/ Hooded Seal *Cystophora cristata*
Length 2-2.6 m (6.6-8.6 ft)

Dugongs and Manatees
ORDER SIRENIA

There are only four species in this order, separated into two families, the dugongs or Dugongidae, containing a single species, and the manatees or Trichechidae with three species. They are all plant-eating animals living in coastal waters and estuaries. Their smooth, bulbous bodies resemble those of other sea mammals and they carry large stores of blubber. The eyes and ear openings are small. They have retained their fore flippers but the hind flippers have been lost. The tail is horizontally flattened to form a paddle-like tail fluke. The dugong has a straight or slightly incurved trailing edge to its tail.

Dugong

The dugong lives in the shallow coastal waters of the south-west Pacific and Indian Oceans from the Red Sea to northern Australia. It is a large animal although it varies considerably in length and weight. Dugongs have smooth, grey-brown skin, a large head, and a fleshy, divided muzzle which conceals its two tusks.

It is a shy, docile animal and has almost been driven to extinction by humans hunting it for its flesh and tusks. It spends much of its time either resting on the bottom or grazing on the sea grasses which it probably chews between the upper and lower palates.

Its breeding biology is not well known but it probably gives birth to a single young in the water after a period of about thirteen months.

Order Sirenia - dugongs and manatees (4 species)
Family/Species Dugongidae - dugongs (1 species)
/Dugong (Sea Cow) *Dugong dugon*
Length 1-4 m (3-13 ft)

American Manatee

There are three species of manatees and this one, living as it does along the Atlantic coast of the Americas from Florida to Guyana, is also known as the West Indian manatee or the Caribbean manatee. The American manatee is a heavier-built animal than the dugong and has a smooth, hairless, silvery grey skin. It can also be distinguished from the dugong by the shape of its tail fluke which is smooth and oval rather than notched. On each of its fore flippers it has three rudimentary nails which are used to help it gather its food.

Found in estuaries and rivers as well as in shallow coastal waters, manatees feed at night on bottom-growing plant material, also taking in some small animals as it eats. During the day they rest on the bed of the sea or river but, because they are air-breathing mammals, they are obliged to surface every few minutes.

Although manatees do sometimes gather in social groups and pups will stay with their mothers for as long as eighteen months, they are more often observed as single animals. The breeding biology of manatees, especially that of the males, is not well known but, approximately a year after mating, the cow gives birth, in the water, to a single calf which is suckled for twelve to eighteen months even though it is able to feed on plants long before this. It seems that cows may mate with more than one male, a process which is known as polyandry.

Order Sirenia - dugongs and manatees (4 species)
Family/Species Trichechidae - manatees (3 species)
 /American Manatee *Trichechus manatus*
Length 2.5-4 m (8-13 ft)

Whales and Dolphins
ORDER CETACEA

The seventy-six species of whales, dolphins, and porpoises are the most fully adapted of the aquatic mammals to life in the water where they spend all of their time. The fast-swimming species of dolphins and porpoises have the most perfectly streamlined bodies. With their fatty dorsal fins, well-developed fore flippers and no visible hind limbs, many cetaceans, especially dolphins and porpoises, are fish-like in appearance. They are still mammals, however, and need to breathe air but, at high speed, instead of swimming along at the surface, which would use more energy and slow them down, they leap clear of the water to take a gulp of air. The nostrils, or 'blowhole', are situated on top of the head (except in sperm whales); when the animals submerge, the blowhole is sealed by air-filled chambers in the nasal passages. Among the baleen whales, the blowhole takes the form of a double slit while, in toothed whales, there is only a single nostril. When a whale surfaces to breathe, spent air is forced from the air passages out through the blowhole resulting in the characteristic plume of spray or 'blow'. Each species of whale has a slightly different arrangement of its nasal opening so that the blow may be different in every case.

The toothed whales, together with the river dolphins, dolphins, and porpoises, comprise the largest group (suborder Odontoceti) containing some sixty-six species. As their name suggests, their often beak-like jaws usually contain teeth - in some species as many as 200 - and they feed mainly on fishes and squid which come their way, locating them by emitting a series of ultrasonic clicks which bounce off their prey, in much the same way as the sonar used by bats.

The baleen whales (suborder Mysticeti) only number ten species in three families, but these whales are the largest of all. It is thought by many scientists that such huge animals could only have evolved in water because, to have supported their enormous body weight on land, they would have needed such massive legs that they would hardly have been able to move around. Baleen whales sieve their tiny food from the water using the baleen plates which have evolved from the skin of the palate. The plates vary in length and thickness from species to species depending upon the size and type of food they consume.

All whales mate and give birth to their young in the water. Usually, only a single offspring is produced but occasionally twins are born. Interestingly, many aspects of the breeding biology of whales seem to be related to their diet. For example, the time between conception and birth of the young is considerably shorter among species which feed upon fish or plankton than it is among the squid eaters. Similarly, the time for which the young are suckled varies according to diet, and even the number of females with which a male mates may be affected in much the same way.

The oceans around the polar and subpolar regions are richer in food than in the tropics. Consequently, many species migrate to seas in the high latitudes to feed during the relatively short polar summers and then return to warmer waters to breed. Some of the smaller cetaceans, however, seem to be able to survive in cool waters throughout the year.

Boutu

The boutu or Amazon dolphin inhabits the muddy rivers and streams of the Amazon basin. It is one of the five species of river dolphins of the family Platanistidae which are found in the rivers of South America and Asia. Although they are all similar in appearance, they are probably not closely related and their similarity has developed because they all tend to live in much the same way in comparable environments - this is known as convergent evolution. The boutu tends to be pinkish in colour, especially on its underside, although the upper parts may be darker, possibly as a response to strong sunlight. It has a long, slender but strong beak, rather like a crocodile's, which is fringed with short bristles and contains about 100 conical, pointed teeth.

The river dolphins are the most primitive members of the order and the boutu, like the other members of the group, has a relatively underdeveloped dorsal fin. The fore flippers still show the traces of their hand-like origins, and the bones in its neck are not fused together as they are in most other cetaceans, so the neck is quite flexible. River dolphins have poor vision and some species can only distinguish between light and dark. The boutu can see fairly well, however, and feeds mainly on small fishes and crustaceans which it can locate with great accuracy using its sonar system.

Little is known about the social behaviour and breeding biology of the boutu although they probably live in pairs or as solitary individuals and give birth to their young between July and September, suckling them for about a year.

Order Cetacea - whales, dolphins, and porpoises (76 species)
Family/Species Platanistidae - river dolphins (5 species)/Boutu (Amazon Dolphin) *Inia geoffrensis*
Length 1.8-2.7 m (6-9 ft)

Ganges Dolphin

The Ganges dolphin inhabits the rivers and streams of India, Nepal, and Bangladesh, especially the river systems of the Ganges and Brahmaputra. It is light to dark greyish brown in colour and tends to be paler on its underside. The forehead is pronounced, and the long beak may reach as much as 46 centimetres (18 inches), that is, about a fifth of its total length. It is largely the beak, which may contain as many as 120 teeth, that accounts for the fact that female Ganges dolphins are a little longer than the males.

The Ganges dolphin is nearly blind - the eyes have lost their lenses and the visual nerve has degenerated so that it can only distinguish from which direction light is coming and can not actually make out objects at all. But, in the murky waters of its home, this matters little, and it finds its prey of fishes and shrimps using its highly accurate echolocation system, hunting mainly by night and in the evening. Oddly, it usually swims on its side but returns to the normal position when it surfaces to breathe after dives which range in duration from the normal 45 seconds to as long as 3 minutes. They are solitary animals although pairs or even groups of up to six have been seen.

Ganges dolphins mate in autumn and then, nine or ten months later, the single pup is born which is suckled for a further eight or nine months. Although the Ganges dolphin is not yet an endangered species, new dam systems on the rivers may threaten its existence in the future.

Order Cetacea - whales, dolphins, and porpoises (76 species)
Family/Species Platanistidae - river dolphins (5 species)/Ganges Dolphin (Ganges Susu) *Platanista gangetica*
Length 1.5-2.6 m (5-8.5 ft)

Whitefin Dolphin

The whitefin dolphin's skin is a medium greyish-blue colour on the uppersides and flanks with a paler or even white belly. Its long beak contains as many as 140 teeth and is slightly upturned at the tip. This river dolphin inhabits the muddy bottomed rivers, mainly the Yangtze, of China as well as Lake Tungting. It has been a protected species since 1975 but, although its numbers are not known accurately, it still seems to be declining probably as a result of dam building on the Yangtze.

Like some other river dolphins, it is effectively blind and locates its prey of fish and shrimps by emitting high-frequency clicks which bounce back off its target. Some shrimps are found by probing in the mud with its beak. Little is known about the breeding behaviour of the whitefin dolphin but it is thought that they move up swollen streams to breed during the summer rainy season. The young are thought to be born some ten or twelve months after mating has occurred.

Order Cetacea - whales, dolphins, and porpoises (76 species)

Family/Species Platanistidae - river dolphins (5 species)/Whitefin Dolphin *Lipotes vexillifer*

Length 2-2.4 m (6.6-8 ft)

Common Porpoise

The common or harbour porpoise inhabits the shallow coastal waters and estuaries of the North Atlantic and North Pacific Oceans as well as the Bering, Baltic, Black, and Mediterranean Seas. The skin on the upper side of its body is dark grey, its sides are a paler grey, and it is white on its belly. These torpedo-shaped sea mammals lack the characteristic beaks of the dolphins.

They are gregarious animals, living in groups of about fifteen, and communicate vocally with one another. They feed on relatively small schooling fishes, such as mackerel and herring, which they locate by sonar-like clicks. The prey is usually swallowed whole. Sadly, because of their feeding habits, they often fall victim to the nets of fishermen which usually results in the death of the animal but it is not known how this has affected their numbers. They are also quite frequently found stranded on beaches. Harbour porpoises show altruistic behaviour within the school, and the group will attempt to come to the assistance of any individual that seems to be in trouble.

The breeding behaviour of harbour porpoises is not well known although it is thought that they probably do not pair for life. There may be a male sexual cycle, however. At mating time, males and females court by swimming together and caressing one another. The calf is born about eleven months after mating has taken place and it is then suckled for a further eight months. The mother lies on her side at the water's surface so that the calf can breathe easily while it is feeding.

Order Cetacea - whales, dolphins, and porpoises (76 species)
Family/Species Phocaenidae - porpoises (6 species)/ Common Porpoise (Harbour Porpoise) *Phocoena phocoena*
Length 1.4-1.8 m (4.6-6 ft)

Dall's Porpoise

The Dall's porpoise is an altogether bigger and more heavily built animal than the common porpoise or, indeed, most other porpoises. The lower jaw bone on its small head tends to undershoot the upper jaw slightly. Its skin is largely black but there is a conspicuous white patch on the underside which may extend up the flanks. The dorsal fin, too, which is larger and more hook shaped than that of the common porpoise, may also have a white patch or may even be entirely white. Dall's porpoise inhabits coastal and deeper oceanic waters of the North Pacific and Bering Sea from southern Japan to southern California. They are often attracted towards ships and, unfortunately, large numbers of Dall's porpoises become entangled in the nets of Japanese fishermen and drown. Once again, it is not known what effects these deaths have on the overall population of the species.

Like most other porpoises, this mammal usually lives in small schools of about four individuals although it may gather in larger groups of up to fifteen and, when it is migrating northwards in summer or southwards in winter, as many as 100 or more animals may swim together. Probably using echolocation to pinpoint their prey, Dall's porpoises feed on several species of oceanic fishes, especially hake, as well as squid.

Little is known about the breeding biology but it seems that mating may take place at any time of the year and the offspring are born about a year later. The young may be suckled for as long as two years so that a cow can only reproduce about once every three years.

Order Cetacea - whales, dolphins, and porpoises
(76 species)
Family/Species Phocoenidae - porpoises (6 species)/
Dall's Porpoise (True's Porpoise) *Phocoenoides dalli*
Length 1.8-2.3 m (6-7.5 ft)

Finless Porpoise

As its name suggests, the finless porpoise lacks the dorsal fin which is found in the other five species of the porpoise family. Instead, the adult has a series of rounded projections (tubercles) along its back just behind where the fin would normally be. It seems that young finless porpoises may ride on the backs of their mothers attached to these tubercles. It differs from other porpoises, too, in having a much more rounded forehead, like that of some species of whales, with a distinguishable beak. The finless porpoise is greyish to blackish in colour and its fins are larger and less triangular than those of other porpoises.

Finless porpoises occupy the coastal waters, estuaries, and rivers of the Indo-pacific region including eastern and south-east Asia, Pakistan, Borneo, and Korea, the Yangtze River, and the East China Sea. An active and agile swimmer, this animal makes short dives in search of its food of squid and fishes as well as seeking out crustaceans on the muddy bottoms of rivers and estuaries. Finless porpoises are often seen alone or in pairs but they may gather together in schools of up to ten animals when they happen to be feeding together.

Once again, little is known about the breeding behaviour of these animals but it is thought that the young is born about eleven months after conception and a female may give birth about once every two years.

Order Cetacea - whales, dolphins, and porpoises
(76 species)
Family/Species Phocoenidae - porpoises (6 species)/
Finless Porpoise (Black Porpoise) *Neophocaena*
phocoenoides
Length 1.4-1.8 m (4.6-6 ft)

Indo-pacific Humpbacked Dolphin

The Indo-pacific humpbacked dolphin inhabits the warm coastal waters, as well as the estuaries and swamps of the Indian Ocean and south-western Pacific region from East Africa to Indonesia and southern China, and it is also found in the Yangtze River. It is a relatively small species with a stout, torpedo-shaped body and, as its name suggests, a pronounced fatty hump on the middle of its back on which is placed the small dorsal fin, as well as other fatty humps near the tail area. It has a long, slim beak, containing at least 120 teeth, but its 'melon', the forehead bulge of fatty tissue which is thought to be involved in echolocation, is quite small. This animal varies in colour from near white, through cream, to a fairly dark grey. Darker specimens are usually paler below than above and some adults may be spotted.

Living as they do in shallow water, where they hunt for fishes, crustaceans, and molluscs using their echolocation skills, it might be expected that they would be in danger of becoming stranded. It seems, however, that they are able to manoeuvre quite effectively even over sand banks.

Like other dolphins, the Indo-pacific humpbacked dolphin is a gregarious animal living in groups of as many as twenty individuals. Mating probably takes place throughout the year.

Order Cetacea - whales, dolphins, and porpoises (76 species)
Family/Species Delphinidae - dolphins (32 species)/ Indo-pacific Humpbacked Dolphin *Sousa chinensis*
Length 2-3 m (6.5-10 ft)

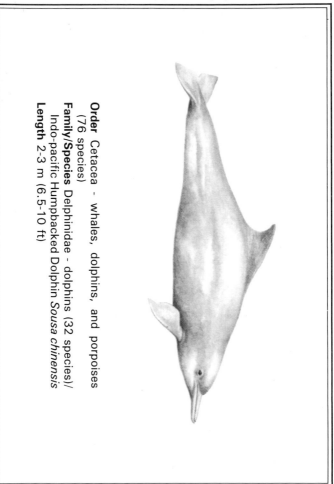

Striped Dolphin

The striped dolphin is comparatively slender and streamlined in shape with a pronounced forehead and a long, slim beak containing ninety to 100 teeth. It varies in colour from dark or bluish grey to brown on its upper parts with paler sides and white undersides. The flippers are black. It gets its name from the various dark stripes and bands on its flanks. The schools of as many as several thousand individuals inhabit the warm tropical, subtropical, and temperate, deep offshore waters of the Atlantic and Pacific Oceans as well as the Mediterranean. They feed on small fishes, squid, and crustaceans. It is possible that they hunt shoaling fishes co-operatively.

The breeding biology of dolphins is not well known and that of the striped dolphin is no exception. It seems likely, however, that mating may take place throughout the year with males mating more than one female. Females breed about once every three years and births take place about a year after conception. The young may be suckled for between nine and eighteen months. The social hierarchy within a school of striped dolphins seems to be based on age.

Order Cetacea - whales, dolphins, and porpoises (76 species)
Family/Species Delphinidae - dolphins (32 species)/Striped Dolphin *Stenella coeruleoalba*
Length 2.4-3 m (8-10 ft)

Common Dolphin

With its distintive markings, wide distribution, and its habit of accompanying ships, this is probably the species that most people consider to be the typical dolphin. It is highly intelligent, friendly, and very active. Common dolphins are found in the coastal and offshore waters throughout the temperate and tropical oceans of the world including the Mediterranean and Black Seas; it is thought that there are several races throughout the world.

They vary considerably in colour from black to brownish black on their upper parts and from cream to white on the underside. The pattern on the flanks takes the shape of an hour glass varying from yellowish at the head end to white or grey at the tail. The sickle-shaped dorsal fin and flippers vary from pale grey to black and there is a dark stripe running from the fore flippers to the long, beak-like jaws. In search of their food, they are able to remain submerged for as long as five minutes, achieving depths of as much as 280 metres (920 feet). They feed on shoaling fishes as well as squid, locating their prey by sonar. The social groups of twenty to 100 animals may gather together into feeding schools of several thousands.

Mating behaviour can take place at any time of the year although most calves are born during the summer after a gestation period of ten or eleven months. The calf may remain with its mother for a good many months while she feeds it.

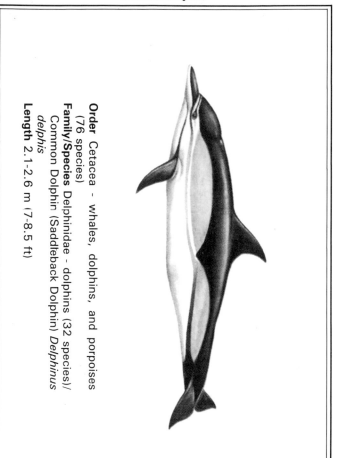

Order Cetacea - whales, dolphins, and porpoises (76 species)
Family/Species Delphinidae - dolphins (32 species)/ Common Dolphin (Saddleback Dolphin) *Delphinus delphis*
Length 2.1-2.6 m (7-8.5 ft)

Bottlenose Dolphin

Most of us are familiar with the bottlenose dolphin from its performances in dolphinariums and its television and cinema appearances. They are friendly, highly intelligent animals which continue to be exploited by humans, not only for food and as a circus act, but also because it is thought to compete with humans for marine resources. Bottlenose dolphins are even used for military purposes. Sadly, too, they seem to be vulnerable to marine pollution in certain areas as well as to the noise disturbance caused by increasing ocean-going traffic. Bottlenose dolphins are found in coastal waters of most of the tropical and temperate oceans of the world.

It is a torpedo-shaped animal with dark-greyish upper parts grading to paler grey on its sides to whitish or pinkish on its belly. It has a long, broad dorsal fin and a comparatively short, broad beak on its strong-looking head. Bottlenose dolphins often appear to be smiling because of the way in which the lower jaw slightly undershoots the upper. They are very communicative animals and live in social groups of about fifteen individuals which may join together to form large feeding schools. They feed on a variety of bottom-living and surface fishes as well as crustaceans.

Breeding takes place at almost any time of the year and, about twelve months after mating, the young is born, assisted by two other adult females which take it to the surface to breathe. The calf is suckled for about another year so that a female is unable to breed more than once about every two years.

Order Cetacea - whales, dolphins, and porpoises
(76 species)
Family/Species Delphinidae - dolphins (32 species)/
Bottlenose Dolphin *Tursiops truncatus*
Length 3-4.2 m (10-14 ft)

Killer Whale

Despite its name, the killer whale or orca, is the largest member of the dolphin family and is hardly dangerous to humans. It is found in the cooler coastal waters throughout most of the world's oceans where it preys upon fishes, squid, sea lions, penguins, and even whales. It is a strongly built but still essentially torpedo-shaped animal with a broad, rounded head, no beak, forty or fifty teeth in its jaws, and rounded flippers. The male is generally a little longer and considerably heavier than the female and possesses the characteristic, very long, triangularly shaped dorsal fin while that of the female is much shorter and sickle shaped. Its skin is largely black in colour but it has white undersides and white patches on its flanks and above its eyes. Killer whales, too, have been trained to perform tricks in dolphinariums - a spectacular sight.

Schools of killer whales will co-operate in pursuit of fishes, herding them into shallow water, at the same time slapping the water with their flippers or even breaching, as well as emitting a variety of clicks and squeals. They will travel in search of the most food-rich parts of the oceans at high latitudes.

Killer whales tend to live in pods of extended family groups with the females, especially, staying with the group. About fifteen months after mating the calf is born, to be suckled by its mother for about a further year. Consequently, a female can usually only give birth to one offspring about every three years although a gap of about eight years between calvings is more typical.

Order Cetacea - whales, dolphins, and porpoises
(76 species)
Family/Species Delphinidae - dolphins (32 species)/
Killer Whale (Orca; Grampus) *Orcinus orca*
Length 6-9 m (20-30 ft)

Long-finned Pilot Whale

The long-finned pilot or pothead whale is found in coastal, temperate waters throughout much of the North Atlantic as well as the southern oceans so that the two populations of the same species are widely separated in their distribution. It gets its name from its unusually long, narrow, sickle-shaped flippers. It is a strongly built animal with a square-shaped bulbous head and a very short beak in which the upper lip slightly overshoots the lower. It has a comparatively short, sickle-shaped dorsal fin. The male may be almost twice the weight of the female. In colour, the long-finned pilot whale is essentially dark grey or black with a paler greyish-white patch on the belly and a similarly coloured small patch on its sides. Pilot whales seem to be particularly susceptible to becoming stranded on the coast although precisely why this should occur remains a mystery.

They are particularly vocal animals and make a wide variety of sounds, some of which are used in their echolocation techniques. They eat mainly squid but also feed on fishes, such as cod and turbot. They live in close-knit groups of six or more individuals but they can congregate in schools numbering several hundred. About sixteen months after mating, the female pilot whale gives birth to her calf which is then suckled for more than a year.

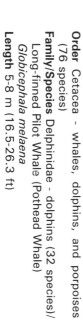

Order Cetacea - whales, dolphins, and porpoises (76 species)
Family/Species Delphinidae - dolphins (32 species)/ Long-finned Pilot Whale (Pothead Whale) *Globicephala melaena*
Length 5-8 m (16.5-26.3 ft)

Risso's Dolphin

The alternative name of Risso's dolphin, grampus, which is also sometimes applied to the killer whale, may be derived from the Latin *crassus piscis*, meaning fat fish. This name is not hard to understand. It is a robustly built, torpedo-shaped animal which is broader in front of its central, sickle-shaped dorsal fin than it is behind, tapering quite markedly towards the tail. It has a blunt head with no beak and quite a pronounced 'melon'; there is a crease down the forehead to the upper lip. In colour, it ranges from mid- to dark grey on its upper parts and sides but the belly and chest areas are usually white. The head of an older adult may be near white.

The flanks of Risso's dolphin are usually covered with scars which seem to have been made by other members of the species because the pattern of tooth marks correspond - there are no teeth in the upper jaw and only three or four on each side of the lower. Risso's dolphins seem to form quite stable social groups. Apparently, this member of the family Delphinidae feeds mainly on a diet of squid.

Order Cetacea - whales, dolphins, and porpoises (76 species)
Family/Species Delphinidae - dolphins (32 species)/ Risso's Dolphin (Grampus) *Grampus griseus*
Length 3-4 m (10-13 ft)

Pygmy Sperm Whale

Pygmy sperm whales inhabit the oceanic waters of warm, temperate, subtropical, and tropical seas throughout the world and they are quite regularly found stranded on the beaches of such countries as the United States, Australia, and South Africa. Little is known, however, of their migratory movements, if any, throughout those waters. Like the other two species of sperm whale, the pygmy sperm whale has an undershot lower jaw and the animal does seem to resemble a rather fat, square-headed shark. It is largely dark grey in colour on its upper parts grading to a greyish white on its belly. The dorsal fin is short and sickle shaped while the paddle-shaped flippers are set well forward, just behind its head region. As in all sperm whales, the body tapers quite sharply towards the tail. Blubber and muscle constitute more than 50 per cent of the animal's total body weight.

A slow-moving toothed whale, the pygmy sperm whale, or lesser sperm whale as it is also called, dives to depths of up to 100 metres (330 feet) in search of its food of squid, fishes, and crabs but it is not known how prey is captured. This sperm whale also feeds in relatively shallow water. Its upper jaw is usually toothless but there are at least twelve pairs of teeth in the lower jaw which probably erupt when the animal reaches adulthood.

Little is known about their breeding habits but it is thought that birth takes place in spring between nine and eleven months after conception. The female may be mated again while she is still suckling her calf which she does for about a year.

Order Cetacea - whales, dolphins, and porpoises
(76 species)
Family/Species Physeteridae - sperm whales (3
species)/Pygmy Sperm Whale (Lesser Sperm Whale)
Kogia breviceps
Length 3-3.4 m (10-11 ft)

Dwarf Sperm Whale

Smallest of the sperm whales, the dwarf or Owen's pygmy sperm whale is similar in colour and general shape to the pygmy sperm whale but it usually has a smaller and more rounded head with the flippers set slightly further back on the body. Although examination of the stomach contents of dead individuals has revealed prey species which are known to live at depths of 250 metres (800 feet), it is thought that this animal generally feeds at depths not exceeding 100 metres (330 feet) in the waters over the continental shelf of tropical and subtropical seas. Again, little is known of its habits and biology, nor how it captures its prey of fish and squid, but it does have eleven pairs of teeth in its undershot lower jaw.

Dwarf sperm whales probably form schools of up to ten individuals which may comprise adults of both sexes, females and their offspring, or immatures. The breeding habits may be much the same as those of the pygmy sperm whale.

Order Cetacea - whales, dolphins, and porpoises (76 species)
Family/Species Physeteridae - sperm whales (3 species)/Dwarf Sperm Whale (Owen's pygmy sperm whale) *Kogia simus*
Length 2.4-2.7 m (8-9 ft)

Sperm Whale

The sperm whale is the biggest of all the toothed whales. The huge head of the sperm whale may be as much as a third of its total body length and it is the head which contains the spermaceti organ that characterizes the animal. Most of the upper part of the head is filled with a waxy substance which is thought to be involved in controlling the buoyancy of the animal as well as in its highly effective echolocation system. Distinct from all other whales, the blowhole emerges at the tip of the snout.

In search of its diet of bottom-dwelling squid, the sperm whale is the champion diver among the aquatic mammals, possibly achieving depths of more than 2000 metres (6600 feet). As it dives into the cooler waters, the waxy spermaceti oil shrinks causing the head of the animal to become more dense and allowing it to dive to greater depths more easily. As it ascends, the reverse occurs. The skin around the head of sperm whales is often scarred with sucker-shaped marks, indicating that sperm whales tackle very large squid which do not give up without a fierce fight.

Sperm whales live throughout the temperate and tropical waters of the world's oceans, migrating towards the poles in spring and returning in autumn, although the males may move to higher latitudes and dive to greater depths to feed, possibly to leave the richer feeding grounds to females and calves. Adult bulls return to tropical waters in winter where they compete to gather together a harem of females and their young. Normally a single calf is born about sixteen months after conception and it is suckled for up to two years.

Order Cetacea - whales, dolphins, and porpoises (76 species)
Family/Species Physeteridae - sperm whales (3 species)/Sperm Whale (Cachalot) *Physeter catodon*
Length 11-20 m (36-66 ft)

Beluga

The beluga is one of only two species in the white whale family, the other being the extraordinary narwhal. The adult, which is creamy white in colour, is a plump-bodied animal with a noticeable 'melon' and a short snout on the small head. There is no dorsal fin, but a ridge, which is often scarred by encounters with ice, runs along the back instead. This white whale is capable of a variety of facial expressions which are thought to be used in communication. Adults have thirty-two to forty teeth which are often very worn and may be more important in communication than for feeding. It has a discernible neck which is very flexible.

The beluga inhabits shallow coastal waters, estuaries, and rivers of the arctic and subarctic seas where it will even swim under pack ice, breaking through to breathe. It feeds on bottom-living crustaceans and molluscs which it may dislodge by suction or by squirting jets of water, but schools of belugas will co-operate to round up shoaling fishes nearer the surface.

Belugas are highly social animals communicating by a wide variety of sounds so that they were once given the name of 'sea canaries'. During their southward migrations in winter, belugas may gather in schools of hundreds; returning northwards in summer to feed. The dark reddish-brown calves are born in summer about fourteen months after the female has been mated in spring. The mother suckles her offspring for at least a year so that she is unable to breed more often than about once every three years.

Order Cetacea - whales, dolphins, and porpoises (76 species)

Family/Species Monodontidae - white whales (2 species)/Beluga (White Whale) *Delphinapterus leucas*

Length 4-6 m (13-20 ft)

Narwhal

The scientific name of the narwhal, *Monodon monoceros* means 'single tooth, single horn'. Although this name is slightly misleading, because narwhals actually have two non-functional teeth in the upper jaw, the left-hand incisor of the male, especially, grows into a long, spiralled, downward-angled tusk which thrusts through a hole in its upper lip. In other respects, the overall body form of the narwhal is similar to that of the beluga. Its skin is unusually coloured in a basically bluish grey or brownish hue, mottled with cream, grey, and black. The belly is paler and the whole animal whitens as it grows older. Narwhals inhabit coastal waters, open sea, and pack ice areas in a patchy distribution throughout the high Arctic Ocean.

The female may have a short tusk, but in neither sex is the tusk used in feeding. The diet of squid, crabs, shrimps, and fishes are probably captured by sucking. The tusks are thought to be used by the males for display purposes in dominating other males to establish the social hierarchy and for impressing females prior to mating. The males even seem to do battle with one another using their tusks rather like the lances of knights of old. Narwhals form social groups of six to ten animals which may gather in larger aggregations during migration.

After mating in early spring, the dark-grey narwhal calves are born during the summer of the following year and they are suckled by the mothers for about two years.

Order Cetacea - whales, dolphins, and porpoises (76 species)
Family/Species Monodontidae - white whales (2 species)/Narwhal *Monodon monoceros*
Length 4-6 m (13-20 ft)

Northern Bottlenose Whale

The northern bottlenose whale is found throughout the deep offshore waters of the North Atlantic and Arctic Oceans where, in summer, it is found as far north as the edge of the polar ice and southwards to the New York coast and the Cape Verde Islands in the winter. It is a more heavily built, round-bodied animal than some of the other beaked whales. As its name suggests, it has an obvious beak which, in adults, contains only two teeth in the lower jaw although these may be so deeply embedded in the gum that they can not be seen. The adults have a very well-developed 'melon' or bulbous forehead which becomes more exaggerated and paler in colour with age. This led Norwegian whalers to give them the name of barrelhead or greyhead. The skin colour varies from greyish brown to cream on the upper parts with a paler grey belly. A large female may be bigger than a small male but, generally, males are larger than females.

On the whole, the beaked whales are elusive and little-known animals but the biology and social behaviour of the northern bottlenose whale are more fully understood. This animal can dive to depths at least as great and possibly greater than any other marine mammal and can remain submerged for periods of up to two hours in search of its prey of squid, cuttlefish, fishes, and some starfishes. In the North Atlantic, groups of two to four animals have been seen although they may gather in social units of as many as twenty individuals. Mating usually takes place in April when the calf from the previous year is also born. The youngster is suckled for about a year.

Order Cetacea - whales, dolphins, and porpoises (76 species)
Family/Species Ziphiidae - beaked whales (18 species)/ Northern Bottlenose Whale *Hyperoodon ampullatus*
Length 7-10 m (23-33 ft)

Cuvier's Beaked Whale

Cuvier's beaked whale is smaller and more slenderly built than the northern bottlenose, tapering markedly towards its tail end. Its rather goose-like beak, from which it derives its alternative name of goose-beaked whale, is less obvious than that of the bottlenose because the head does not have the bulbous forehead and is more concave in shape. From the top of the snout to the dorsal fin the skin is usually a creamy white colour. The rest of the body is usually darker but may be very variable, ranging from yellowish to reddish brown to dark blue-grey with white patches on the sides and belly caused by parasitic lampreys. It may be heavily scarred with the tooth marks of others of its kind. Males may be distinguished from females by the two teeth which protrude from the lower jaw. Cuvier's beaked whale is found throughout the oceans of the world, inhabiting the deep, tropical and temperate waters.

Like the other members of the beaked whale family, this species dives to considerable depths for long periods in search of its food of squid and deep-water fishes. The breeding biology is not well known but calves seem to be born throughout the year.

Order Cetacea - whales, dolphins, and porpoises (76 species)
Family/Species Ziphiidae - beaked whales (18 species)/Cuvier's Beaked Whale (Goose-beaked Whale) *Ziphius cavirostris*
Length 6.4-7 m (21-23 ft)

Shepherd's Beaked Whale

Shepherd's beaked whale is somewhat larger than Sowerby's and belongs to a different genus. It is generally dark, greyish brown in colour with a paler belly. Like many other beaked whales, few of them have ever been seen in the wild, and it was not identified at all until 1933. Its biology and habits are poorly known. It has a long, slender beak with two conically shaped teeth protruding from the tip of the lower jaw. In addition, it has twenty-four or more conical teeth in the lower jaw as well as about 20 similarly shaped teeth in the upper. It is thought to live around the coasts and in the open ocean of the seas around the South Pole although, because only about ten living specimens have ever been seen, until the 1970s, it was thought to be confined to the seas around New Zealand. Now, however, specimens have been found around Argentina, Chile, and Tierra del Fuego. Presumably its habits and breeding biology are similar to those of other beaked whales.

Order Cetacea - whales, dolphins, and porpoises (76 species)
Family/Species Ziphiidae - beaked whales (18 species)/Shepherd's Beaked Whale *Tasmacetus shepherdi*
Length 6-6.6 m (20-22 ft)

Sowerby's Beaked Whale

Sowerby's beaked whale is one of twelve species of the genus *Mesoplodon* which are characterized by having a single tooth set in the mid-point of each side of the lower jaw. These are much less prominent in females than in males. It is these teeth which are used to distinguish between the different species of this genus which are otherwise hard to tell apart at sea. The beak is comparatively short.

The distribution of this whale has been the matter of some argument. It is certainly found in the cool coastal waters of the North Atlantic but it has been suggested that it was once found in the North Sea, giving the animal its alternative name of North Sea beaked whale. They tend to live in deep water and avoid any contact with ships so they have not often been observed in the wild and their biology is not well known.

This whale tends to be dark grey or blackish in colour, possibly with paler underparts, and it is usually scarred from the teeth of other members of the species as well as patched with the marks of attending parasites. It has a fairly rounded body with comparatively small flippers and a small, sickle-shaped dorsal fin.

Like other beaked whales, they probably feed mainly on fishes and squid. It probably gives birth to its young in the southern wintering areas to which it migrates. At birth, the calves may be as long as 2 metres (6.6 feet).

Order Cetacea - whales, dolphins, and porpoises (76 species)
Family/Species Ziphiidae - beaked whales (18 species)/Sowerby's Beaked Whale (North Sea Beaked Whale) *Mesoplodon bidens*
Length 5-6 m (16.5-20 ft)

Baird's Beaked Whale

Baird's beaked whale is the largest member of its family, weighing in at as much as 15 tonnes for an adult female. Unlike the other beaked whales, this animal has a very characteristic beak with an undershot lower jaw from which two pairs of functional teeth protrude near the tip - the front pair is larger than the pair behind. Females have these teeth, too, although they are smaller. The adult males, which are generally smaller than the females, are usually badly scarred as a result of competition between rivals for breeding females. In colour, they are brownish or bluish grey with paler patches on the belly and throat; the female tends to be paler than the male.

Baird's beaked whales inhabit the temperate deep waters of the North Pacific Ocean where they live in groups of between six and thirty animals led by a dominant male, and feed upon squid, octopuses, fishes, crustaceans, and other invertebrates.

It is thought that the animals mate in mid-summer while they are in the warm waters of the southern extent of their range. The period from conception to the birth of the calf seems to be somewhat variable and is quoted as being anything between ten and seventeen months. Unusually, Baird's beaked whales migrate northwards in the winter to the cooler waters of the Bering Sea around the Pribilof Islands and Alaska. These movements, in the opposite directions to those of the majority of whales, may be related to supplies of their preferred food items.

Order Cetacea - whales, dolphins, and porpoises (76 species)
Family/Species Ziphiidae - beaked whales (18 species)/Baird's Beaked Whale (Northern Giant Bottlenose Whale) *Berardius bairdi*
Length 10-12 m (33-39 ft)

Grey Whale

The grey whale or California grey whale is the only representative of its family. As its name suggests, it is mid to dark grey in colour with some mottling and it is usually covered with parasites, such as barnacles and lice. It has no dorsal fin but there is a line of bumps along the lower part of its back in roughly the place where the small dorsal fins of other baleen whales are found. It is found in the coastal waters, often quite close to the shore, of the northern Pacific in two populations on the eastern and western sides of the ocean. Large males may be longer than small females but a female grey whale in calf may weigh almost twice as much as the male. Like the other baleen whales, it feeds by sieving out small invertebrates from the water using its yellowish white baleen plates that are suspended from the slightly arched upper jaw. Unusually, it feeds on bottom-dwelling worms and other animals which are disturbed as the whale stirs up the sediment with its snout.

Grey whales probably perform the longest migrations of all the cetaceans, travelling as much as 20 000 kilometres (12 500 miles) between their summer feeding grounds in arctic waters and the winter calving grounds in the south. Mating takes place in shallow waters at the breeding grounds and the calf is born twelve months later. On occasions, it has been reported that a second male attends the mating, and that he supports the female during copulation. Two months after its birth, the calf follows its mother on the northward migration.

Order Cetacea - whales, dolphins, and porpoises (76 species)
Family/Species Eschrichtidae - grey whales (1 species)/Grey Whale (California Grey Whale) *Eschrichtius robustus*
Length 12-15 m (39-49 ft)

Minke Whale

The Minke whale is the smallest member of the rorqual whale family and has a much narrower head and snout than the others. There are numerous grooves running the length of the throat towards the belly and these grooves or folds seem to allow the throat of the animal to expand when it is feeding. Its food consists mainly of planktonic crustaceans, which are sieved from the water through the mainly whitish plates of the baleen apparatus, although animals living in more temperate waters do feed on fishes and squid. Its skin is basically a dark bluish grey on the upper parts with a creamy white belly and undersides of the comparatively small, narrow flippers. There is also usually a white patch on the upper side of the flippers. The dorsal fin takes the form of a small, backward-pointing triangle set well towards the tail of the animal.

The Minke whale inhabits mainly shallow waters, estuaries, rivers, and inland seas throughout all the world's oceans from the poles to the tropics. Like most other rorqual whales, the Minke will travel long distances on its migration from the summer feeding grounds in polar seas to the winter breeding areas in more temperate or tropical regions.

Breeding may possibly take place at any time of the year although the single calf, conceived about ten months earlier in the breeding grounds, is usually born in the winter and then suckled for about six months. It accompanies its mother on the migration to the feeding areas.

Order Cetacea - whales, dolphins, and porpoises
(76 species)
Family/Species Balaenopteridae - rorqual whales (6
species)/Minke Whale *Balaenoptera acutorostrata*
Length 8-11 m (26-36 ft)

Sei Whale

Except that it is considerably larger, the Sei whale is not dissimilar in appearance to the Minke whale. It is dark grey above and pale beneath but the plates of its baleen apparatus tend to be a greyish black colour with paler fringes. Its head is somewhat broader, flatter, and bigger than that of its cousin. It, too, has numerous throat grooves which allow its mouth and throat cavity to expand when it is feeding. Sei whales are found in the surface waters of the open oceans from the tropics towards, but not reaching, the polar regions. They tend to feed on smaller food items, including the minute copepod crustaceans, which are sieved from the water on the very fine fringes of the baleen plates. They also consume larger crustaceans, such as krill, however, as well as small fishes and squid. They often feed at the surface, skimming along the water with the upper jaw exposed. They are able to swim at considerable speeds, making the most of their streamlined body shape. Their migration patterns and life cycle are probably similar to those of the Minke whale

Family groups of five or six animals often swim together and it appears that the social bond between the pairs is strong, lasting beyond a given breeding season. The single calf is born about a year after conception and is nursed for a further six months or so by the mother until it is weaned.

Order Cetacea - whales, dolphins, and porpoises (76 species)
Family/Species Balaenopteridae - rorqual whales (6 species)/Sei Whale *Balaenoptera borealis*
Length 15-20 m (49-66 ft)

Blue Whale

As its name suggests, this magnificent but endangered animal is a mottled bluish grey in colour and its baleen plates tend to be blackish. At the monstrous weight of as much as 150 tonnes, it is thought by many to be the biggest animal ever to have lived on Earth with the possible exception of one species of dinosaur. Indeed, it is considered that such bulk could only be attained by an aquatic animal, where the water gives it support. Despite its huge size, it is still a filter feeder, straining out vast quantities of small, planktonic crustaceans of a surprisingly restricted number of species. Although blue whales have been fully protected since 1967, their numbers had been reduced so drastically by the whalers, and now even their food supply of krill is threatened with exploitation by humans, so that their future must be in doubt.

It is similar in shape, but not size, to the Sei and Minke whales, and, like them, it has between fifty and ninety grooves on its throat; for such a large aquatic mammal the dorsal fin is very small and is situated near to the tail. It inhabits open oceans throughout the world and migrates regularly from its winter breeding grounds near the tropics to the summer feeding grounds in polar waters where it may consume as much as 4 tonnes of krill every day. In the warm waters of the breeding grounds, mating occurs, and the calf conceived during the previous season is born after a gestation period of about eleven or twelve months.

Order Cetacea - whales, dolphins, and porpoises (76 species)
Family/Species Balaenopteridae - rorqual whales (6 species)/Blue Whale *Balaenoptera musculus*
Length 25-32 m (82-105 ft)

Humpback Whale

The humpback whale is largely black in colour with a paler throat and belly region. Its broad head with characteristic bowed jaw line lacks the central ridge which runs down the snout of other members of the family. The lower jaw protrudes beyond the upper and both bear knobbly lumps. The leading edges of the very long flippers also carry a row of swellings. The dorsal fin is small and backward pointing and is set on a fleshy pad well down the body. It has a smaller number of broader throat grooves than the other rorquals.

It is found in oceanic and coastal waters throughout the world from the poles to the tropics. The humpback is a surprisingly agile animal, leaping into the air for no reason that is as yet known although, on some occasions, this may serve to herd the fishes on which humpbacks living in the northern hemisphere tend to feed. In the krill-rich waters of the south, humpbacks mainly eat these small crustaceans.

Humpbacks are more gregarious than other rorquals and are usually seen in family groups of three or four animals. They are also very communicative and may make contact with other groups over very long distances by producing their extraordinarily eerie, wistful-sounding, and wide-ranging songs which may continue for hours on end. Their migration patterns are basically similar to those of the other rorquals. The single calf is born about a year after mating and is then suckled by the mother for about another year.

Order Cetacea - whales, dolphins, and porpoises
(76 species)
Family/Species Balaenopteridae - rorqual whales (6
species)/Humpback Whale *Megaptera novaeangliae*
Length 15-19 m (49-62.5 ft)

Bowhead Whale

The bowhead whale gets its name from the upwardly curved or bow-shaped jaw line of the huge head. The jaws contain finely fringed baleen plates which, at as much as 4.5 metres (15 feet) long, are the longest of any baleen whale. Consequently, they feed on the smallest planktonic crustaceans of all. It is a member of the right whale family, which contains three species and get their name from the fact that they are large, slow-moving, and float when they are dead, so that they were the 'right whales' for the early whalers to hunt. Not surprisingly, they are now rare and an endangered species.

The bowhead whale is essentially black in colour although it has a variable, creamy white patch on its chin. It can be distinguished from the right whale itself because it lacks the callous-like patches concentrated on the head which are caused by parasites. There are no throat grooves. It may be a vocal animal but little is known of this aspect of its life.

Bowheads mate in early spring as they begin their migrations and, after a gestation period of about ten or twelve months, usually a single calf is born although twins are known. The mother suckles its offspring for about a year.

Order Cetacea - whales, dolphins, and porpoises (76 species)
Family/Species Balaenidae - right whales (3 species)/Bowhead Whale (Greenland Right Whale) *Balaena mysticetus*
Length 15-20 m (49-66 ft)

Glossary

altruistic behaviour behaviour that may benefit another individual without necessarily benefiting the individual behaving altruistically.

anatomy the structure and organization of the body of an animal or plant.

aquatic describing an animal or plant which lives or grows in water.

baleen the horny, triangular plates which hang from each side of the roof of the mouth of baleen whales. They are formed from the transverse ridges which cross the upper palate of many mammals. With their bristly, fringed edges, they are used to strain small, planktonic creatures from the water for food. Baleen is also incorrectly referred to as whalebone.

baleen whale any of the group of toothless whales of the suborder Mysteceti, comprising the families Eschrichtidae, Balaenopteridae, and Balaenidae. They all have baleen plates in their jaws rather than teeth.

blubber the fatty layer which is situated between the skin and muscle of an aquatic mammal and which serves to insulate the animal as well as improving its generally streamlined shape.

breach the way in which an aquatic mammal leaps from the water.

carnivore an animal or plant which feeds mainly on the flesh of other animals.

cartilage the tough, flexible tissue, otherwise known as gristle, which makes up the spine of some fishes, such as sharks, and which is also found over the ends of bones, in joints, and between the vertebrae of other vertebrates.

convergent evolution the process of evolutionary change in which unrelated animals or plants develop similar structures as a result of the similar environmental conditions in which they live or their similar life styles. For example, insects, birds, and bats have all developed wings for powered flight.

copepod any of the group of very small, filter-feeding crustaceans which lack compound eyes and the tough outer covering, and which comprise an important part of the plankton both in the sea and in fresh water.

crustacean any of the mainly aquatic animals, such as crabs or lobsters, which lack a backbone but have jointed legs and are usually protected by a tough, horny outer 'shell'.

delayed implantation the process in which the fertilized egg lies dormant for some period of time in the womb of certain animals, such as seals or badgers, so that birth will occur at the most favourable time following a normal period of development without the offspring growing to too large a size for birth to occur.

dorsal describing the back of an animal.

echolocation the method by which animals, such as whales or bats, pinpoint objects or food items by producing usually high-pitched sounds which bounce back off the object and are received by the animal. The time taken for the sound to return, its frequency, and its direction enable the

animal to locate its quarry as well as its speed
and direction of motion with great accuracy.

ecology the study or science of plants and animals
with regard to their relationships with their
environment and other plants or animals.

evolution the process in which, over long periods
of time, populations of animals and plants change
gradually as characteristics which are well fitted
to their environment are passed on and
emphasized through successive generations.
Ultimately, this leads to new species arising.

fast ice ice which is effectively permanent

gestation period in breeding, the period of time
which elapses between conception and the birth of
the offspring.

haul out the process in which an aquatic mammal,
such as a seal, heaves itself bodily on to land - to
give birth, for example.

herbivore an animal which feeds largely on plant
material.

homoiothermic describing an animal which
maintains its internal body temperature at a
roughly constant level despite changing external
temperatures.

krill one of the various species of reddish-
coloured, shrimp-like crustaceans which occur in
vast numbers especially in the seas of the
Antarctic and which provide food for a number of
sea mammals, including the biggest of them all,
the blue whale.

mammal any animal of the class Mammalia, such as a dog or a whale. Mammals have backbones, are usually covered with a coat of hair to insulate them because they are poikilothermic, and feed their offspring through the early part of life on milk secreted from the mammary glands of the mother.

mammary gland any of the glands on a female mammal which secrete milk to feed a developing offspring during the early part of its life.

mollusc any animal, such as a cockle or a squid, which belongs to the phylum Mollusca. Molluscs lack a backbone and are soft bodied.

pelvis that part of the skeleton of an animal to which the bones of the hind limbs are attached.

physiology the way in which animals or plants function.

plankton any of the many different kinds of animals and plants which drift freely in the sea or freshwater habitats. They are mostly very small or even microscopic but occur in such vast numbers that they provide an important food source for many other animals, including whales.

poikilothermic describing an animal whose internal body temperature varies in response to changing external conditions.

polyandry the condition in which females mate with more than one male.

tail fluke either of the two identical, roughly triangular fins which comprise the tail of a whale and provide the main means of propulsion.

terrestrial describing an animal or plant which lives or grows on land.

toothed whale any of the whales, dolphins, and porpoises of the suborder Odontoceti which comprise the families Platanistidae, Delphinidae, Phocoenidae, Monodontidae, Physeteridae, and Ziphiidae. Many have beak-like jaws and they always possess teeth in some form.

tubercle any small, rounded knob on the skin of an animal.

vertebrate any of the animals which are included in the subphylum Vertebrata, such as fishes, amphibians, reptiles, birds, and mammals, and which are characterized by having a backbone.

Further Reading

Bonner, W N. *Whales*. Blandford Press, Poole, 1980.
Ellis, R. *Dolphins and Porpoises*. Robert Hale, London, 1983.
Hardy, Sir Alister. *Great Waters*. Collins, London, 1967.
Martin, R M. *Mammals of the Sea*. Batsford, London, 1977.
Matthews, L H. *The Natural History of the Whale*. Weidenfeld and Nicolson, London. 1978.

INDEX

Numbers in *italics* refer to illustrations

A

Africa
  East 15, 74
  West 13, 15
Aleutian Islands 26, 32
America
  North 15, 26, 28, 32, 34,
    36, 38, 48, 54, 106
  South 13, 15, 62
Antarctic 15, 16, 44, 52,
  102
Arctic Ocean 15, 34, 38,
  46, 54, 94, 96, 98, 108,
  114, 116
Arctocephalus australis 25
Argentina 40, 102
Asia 15, 34, 62, 72
Atlantic Ocean 13, 24, 36,
  38, 42, 50, 54, 58, 68,
  76, 84, 98, 104
Australasia 15
Australia 15, 30, 40, 56, 88
Azores 42

B

Balaenidae *119*
Balaenoptera acutorostrata
  111
    borealis *113*
    musculus 9, *115*

Balaenopteridae *111-17*
Baltic Sea 68
Bangladesh 64
beluga 94, *95*
Berardius bairdi 107
Bering Sea 27, 68, 70, 106
Black Sea 50, 68, 78
boutu 62, *63*
Brahmaputra 64
breeding 18
Britain 36

C

cachalot *see* whale, sperm
California 32, 48, 70
Callorhinus ursinus 27
Cape Verde Islands 98
Caribbean 13, 15
Cetacea 9, 15, 16, 60,
  63-119
Chile 102
Chordata 9
communication 18
Cystophora cristata 55

D

Delphinapterus leucas 95
Delphinidae 9, *75-87*
Delphinus delphis 79
Denmark strait 54
distribution 14-15

dolphin 6, 7, 15, 16, 19, 20, 60-81, 86-7
  Amazon *see* boutu
  bottlenose 80, *81*
  common 78, 79
  Ganges 64, *65*
  Indo-pacific humpbacked *74, 75*
  Risso's 86, *87*
  river 14, 60-1, 62, *63-7*
  Saddleback *see* common *above*
  striped 76, *77*
  whitefin 66, *67*
dugong 7, 9, 13, 15, 18, 19 20, 56-7
Dugong dugon 57
Dugongidae 56, *57-9*

E
East China Sea 72
Erignathus barbatus 47
Eschrichtidae *109*
Eschrichtius robustus 109
Eumetopias jubata 33
Europe 15, 34
evolution 12-14
extinction 19-20

F
Falkland Islands 24
Faroe Islands 36

G
Galapagos Islands 15, 28
Ganges, River 64
Globicephala melaena 85
grampus *see* orca *and* dolphin, Risso's
Grampus griseus 87
Greenland 34, 54

H
habits 15-19
Halichoerus grypus 37
Hawaii 15
history 12-14
human 19-20
hunting 19
Hydrurga leptonyx 41
Hyperoodon ampullatus 99

I
India 64
Indian Ocean 56, 74
Indonesia 74
Inia geoffrensis 63

J
Japan 28, 32, 70

K
Kogia breviceps 89
  simus 91
Korea 72

Kurile Islands 32

L

Leptonychotes weddelli 53
Linnaeus, Carolus 9
Lipotes vexillifer 67
Lobodon carcinophagus 45

M

Mammalia 9
manatee 7, 9, 13, 15, 18,
    20, 56-9
  American 58, *59*
  Caribbean *see* American
    above
  West Indian *see*
    American *above*
Mediterranean Sea 15, 50,
    68, 76, 78
Megaptera novaeangliae
    117
Mesoplodon 104
  bidens 105
Mirounga angustirostris 49
Moby Dick 92
Monachus monachus 51
Monodon monoceros 96, 97
Monodontidae 95-7
Mysticeti 61

N

narwhal 17, 94, 96, 97
Neophoca cinerea 31

Neophocaena phocoenoides
    73
Nepal 64
New Zealand 102
North Sea 104

O

Odobenidae 22, *35*
Odobenus rosmarus 35
Odontoceti 61
Okhotsk Sea 26
orca 12, 17, 44, 82, *83*, 86
Orcinus orca 12, *83*
Otariidae 22, 25-33

P

Pacific Ocean 14, 24, 28,
    32, 42, 48, 56, 68, 70,
    74, 76, 106, 108
Pagophilus groenlandicus 39
Pakistan 72
Peru 24
Phoca vitulina 43
Phocidae 15, 22, 36, *37-55*
Phocoena dioptrica 12
  phocoena 69
Phocoenidae 12, 69-73
Phocoenoides dalli 71
Physeter catadon 93
Physeteridae 89-93
Pinnipedia 9, 13, 22-55
Platanista gangetica 65
Platanistidae 9, 62, 63-7

pollution 19-20
porpoise 12, 16, 60-1,
    68-81,
  black *see* finless *below*
  common 68, *69*, 70
  Dall's 12, 70, *71*
  finless 72, *73*
  harbour *see* common
    above
  spectacled 12
  True's *see* Dall's *above*
Portugal 36, 54
Pribilof Islands 26, 32, 106
Red Sea 56
Russia 26, 38

S
St Lawrence, Gulf of 36,
    54
San Miguel Island 32
Scandinavia 36, 38
sea cow *see* dugong
sea lion 13, 14, 18, 20,
    22-55
  Australian 30, *31*
  California 28, *29*, 32
  Steller 28, 32, *33*
sea turtle 19
seal 6, 7, 18, 19, 20, 22-55
  Alaskan 26, *27*
  Atlantic *see* grey *below*
  bearded 46, *47*
  Caribbean monk 22

common 42, *43*
crabeater 18, 44, *45*
eared 13, 14, 22-33, *25*
elephant 36, 42
fur 22, 30
grey 36, *37*, 42
hair *see* true *below*
harbour *see* common
    above
harp 38, *39*
hooded 54, *55*
leopard 18, 40, *41*, 42,
    44
Mediterranean monk 50,
    51
northern *see* Alaskan
    above
northern elephant 48, *49*
South American fur 24,
    25
true 13, 14, 15, 22, 23,
    37-55
Weddell 52, *53*
Sirenia 9, 18, 56-9
Sousa chinensis 75
South Africa 14, 40, 88
Spain 46
Stenella coeruleoalba 77
susu, Ganges *see* dolphin,
    Ganges *above*

T
Tasmacetus sheperdi 103

taxonomy 8-12
Trichechidae 56, *59*
Trichechus manatus 59
Tungting, Lake 66
Tursiops truncatus 81

U

*United States of America
89*

W

*walrus 7, 9, 13, 15, 18, 22,
23, 34, 35*
Weddell Sea 52
whale 6, 7, 8, 14, 15, 17,
19, 20, 60-1, 82-119
Baird's beaked 106, *107*
baleen 16, 60, 61, 108,
118
barrelhead *see* northern
bottlenose *below*
beaked 16, 98, *99-107*,
100, 104
blue 7, 9, 20, 114, *115*
bowhead 118, *119*
California grey *see*
grey *below*
Cuvier's beaked 100, *101*
dwarf sperm 90, *91*
goose-beaked *see*
Cuvier's beaked *above*
Greenland right *see*
bowhead *above*

grey 108, *109*
greyhead *see* northern
bottlenose *below*
humpback 116, *117*
killer *see* orca
lesser sperm *see* pygmy
sperm *below*
long-finned pilot 84, *85*
minke 110, *111*, 112, 114
North Sea beaked *see*
Sowerby's beaked
below
northern bottlenose 98,
99, 100
northern giant bottlenose
see Baird's beaked
above
Owen's pygmy sperm
see dwarf sperm *above*
pothead *see* long-finned
pilot *above*
pygmy sperm 88, *89*
right 19, 118, *119*
rorqual 110, *111-17*
sei 112, *113*, 114
Shepherd's beaked 102,
103
Sowerby's beaked 102,
104, *105*
sperm 16, 60, 88, *89-93*,
92
toothed 16, 60
white 16, 94, *95-7*

Y

Yantze River 66, 72, 74

Z

Zalophus californianus 29
Ziphiidae 99-107
Ziphius cavirostris 101